MW00532984

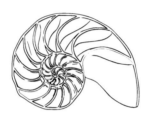

Published by Canon Press
P.O. Box 8729, Moscow, Idaho 83843
800.488.2034 | www.canonpress.com

Dr. Gordon Wilson, *Worldview Guide for Origin of Species*
Copyright © 2017 by Gordon Wilson.
For the Canon Classics edition of the book (2017), go to
www.canonpress.com/books/canon-classics.

Cover design by James Engerbretson
Cover illustration by Forrest Dickison
Interior design by Valerie Anne Bost and James Engerbretson

Printed in the United States of America.

A free end-of-book test and answer key are available for download at
www.canonpress.com/ClassicsQuizzes

17 18 19 20 21 22   9 8 7 6 5 4 3 2 1

WORLDVIEW GUIDE

ORIGIN OF SPECIES

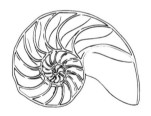

Dr. Gordon Wilson

canonpress
Moscow, Idaho

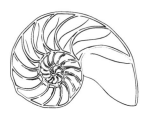

CONTENTS

Introduction 1

The World Around 3

About the Author 5

What Other Notables Said 9

Terms and Argument Summary 13

Worldview Analysis 19

Quotables 37

21 Significant Questions and Answers 39

Further Discussion and Review 51

Taking the Classics Quiz 53

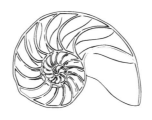

INTRODUCTION

Origin of Species is a must read for Christians in our secularized, Darwin-saturated society. From a factual foundation, Charles Darwin persuasively extrapolates an erroneous explanation of life's diversity and complexity apart from God's handiwork, although there's a lot Darwin argues that his modern-day proponents ignore. Not surprisingly, this naturalistic theory has been the scientific justification behind great secular evils such as eugenics and the holocaust. Christians, using Scripture and science, should study this profoundly influential book thoroughly and cautiously.

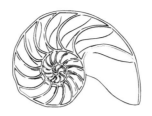

THE WORLD AROUND

Charles Darwin published his first edition of *On the Origin of Species* in 1859. That same year, another Charles (whose surname was Dickens) published his famous book *The Tale of Two Cities*.

An ocean and a half away from them to the west, Mauna Loa, a large volcano in Hawaii, erupted for three hundred days straight. On a less disruptive note, my next-door-neighbor state, Oregon, became the 33rd state to join the Union (fifty-four years after Lewis and Clark arrived there). And, a month before the publication of *On the Origin of Species*, John Brown led an armed raid on Harper's Ferry Armory in West Virginia (just "Virginia" at that time), hoping to spark an uprising of slaves.

Exactly one month before the John Brown incident (who was seeking to free men from physical bondage), David Livingstone, British explorer, physician, and Christian missionary (seeking to free men from spiritual bondage) was the first European to discover Lake Malawi (Lake Nyasa) bordering Tanzania, Mozambique, and Malawi.

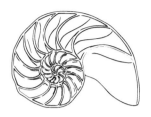

ABOUT THE AUTHOR

Charles Darwin was born into a prosperous British family in 1809. His mother died when he was eight, and his older sisters did most of his rearing. His father, Dr. Robert Darwin was a physician. Charles was classically educated, but the classics bored him—he wanted to see, touch, and inquire into the natural world. His father had other plans. At age sixteen, Charles was sent to the Edinburgh University to receive medical training like his older brother Erasmus. Despite the drudgery of formal lectures, Charles met several professors and other naturalists who had similar scientific interests. His scientific curiosity (particularly regarding geology and entomology) was stoked by these friendships and other experiences (usually outside of class).

It soon dawned on him that he wasn't cut out to be a physician and stopped pursuing medicine. He switched to Cambridge, graduated from there, and decided to become a minister. This was not contrary to Charles's interests, since it was common for clergymen to pursue natural history, and his Christian faith was not yet in crisis (that appears to have happened after his ten-year-old daughter's death in 1851). However, before he entered the church, he received an offer to be a naturalist (and gentleman to Captain FitzRoy) on board the *H.M.S. Beagle*, whose mission was to survey the coastline of South America from 1831 to 1836. A professor encouraged Charles to pursue the job and gave him an enthusiastic recommendation. Over these five years at sea Darwin collected many specimens and took copious field notes (collecting close to two thousand pages of specimen notes, seven hundred pages in his journal, and over five thousand specimen samples). He had time for adventure as well, taking part in the Uruguayan revolution and discovering with horror the savagery of native Americans and the way they were being exterminated. "How great difference between savage & civilized man is—It is greater than between a wild & [a] domesticated animal."[1] He also saw Mount Osorto erupt and witnessed an earthquake and tidal wave destroy the city of Concepcion in Chile; this and other images of suffering deeply impacted Darwin and led to his later agnosticism. He didn't become an evolutionist during the voyage, but his deep thinking, careful observations, experimentation, and correspondence with many scientists over

---

1. Charles Darwin, *The Voyage of the Beagle*, vol. 29 of The Harvard Classics (New York: F.F. Collier and Son, 1909), 210 [chapter 10].

the following two decades led him to formulate and write a long sustained argument for a naturalistic theory of evolution. This was *On the Origin of Species*.

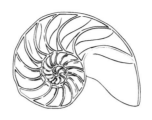

WHAT OTHER
NOTABLES SAID

It is fair to say the reception to Darwin's hypothesis was mixed.

Reverend Luther Tracy Townsend critically comments on *Origin of Species*: "When we ask Mr. Darwin about the evolution of the battery of the electric eel, or about the evolution of the eye of the cuttlefish, or of the eye or ear of a human being, matters that his theory without much hesitation ought to explain, he hastily takes refuge under a confession of ignorance, replying that 'it is impossible to conceive by what steps these wondrous organs have been produced'…. And yet we hear on every hand that the hypotheses of naturalism are established!"[2]

---

2. Luther Tracy Townsend, *Evolution or creation; a critical review of the scientific and scriptural theories of creation and certain related subjects* (New York: Fleming H. Revell, 1896), 54.

Many of Darwin's friends (and his wife) were shocked. Adam Sedgewick writes, "If I did not think you a good tempered & truth loving man I should not tell you that… I have read your book with more pain than pleasure. Parts of it I admired greatly; parts I laughed at till my sides were almost sore; other parts I read with absolute sorrow; because I think them utterly false & grievously mischievous—You have *deserted*—after a start in that tram-road of all solid physical truth—the true method of induction… I have written in a hurry & in a spirit of brotherly love."[3]

Others received the book with excitement, perhaps none more than Thomas Henry Huxley, who became known as "Darwin's Bulldog." He wrote, "Mr. Darwin's hypothesis is not, so far as I am aware, inconsistent with any known biological fact; on the contrary, if admitted, the facts of Development, of Comparative Anatomy, of Geographical Distribution, and of Palaeontology [sic], become connected together, and exhibit a meaning such as they never possessed before; and I, for one, am fully convinced that if not precisely true, that hypothesis is as near an approximation to the truth as, for example, the Copernican hypothesis was to the true theory of the planetary motions."[4]

3. Adam Sedgwick to Charles Darwin, Cambridge, 24 December 1859, in *The Life and Letters of the Reverend Adam Sedgwick*, ed. John Willis Clark and Thomas McKenny Hughes (Cambridge: CUP, 1890), 1:356-57.

4. Thomas Henry Huxley, *Evidence as to Man's Place in Nature* (New York: D. Appleton, 1863), 127.

During the months after the book's release, Darwin, who appears to have had a very nervous temperament already and would even tie plate batteries to his stomach to prevent nausea, declared he was "living in Hell."

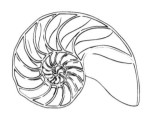

TERMS AND
ARGUMENT SUMMARY

- *Variation* – the tendency of each species to manifest remarkable differences.
- *Natural Selection* – the process by which nature "selects" which variant will survive and which variants won't (since not all can live). The survivors pass their winning traits to the next generation. *Survival of the fittest* is another phrase Darwin uses for this concept.
- *Struggle for existence* – The usual state for all organisms in which more offspring are produced than can survive; this brings organisms in conflict with each other and with the environment. This leads to survival of the fittest.
- *Artificial Selection* – Darwin calls it "variation under domestication." This process is when people, not nature, select what types of animals

survive by encouraging the healthy ones to breed. Domestication is just a long word for animal breeding.

• *Fixity of Species* – the widely held (and wrong) belief that each taxonomic species was fixed at Creation and cannot give rise to other taxonomic species, just to other varieties within that species.

Basically, *On the Origin of Species* is one long sustained argument to persuade the reader of the power of natural selection. Darwin believed natural selection alone could, over eons of time, generate all the diversity of life from just a few or even one life form. He argues that natural selection works by eliminating the least fit members of the same species, just as people regularly do with animals. This "culling" means that environmental conditions ("nature") always choose ("select") which members of a species are best suited to survive, breed, and pass on their traits to the next generation, and which ones are not.

Darwin was a very copious, careful, thoughtful, and intelligent man. He was also patient in building his argument, so don't make a straw man of his work. His foundation is not shaky. At the outset (Chapter 1), he convinces his readers of his reasonableness, breadth of knowledge, and considerable research by describing many verifiable examples of marked variation found in domestic plants and animals. He clearly describes the craft of artificial selection which breeders use to mold plants and animals to their desired aesthetic or useful ends. He gives examples of artificial selection (though he calls it "variation under domestication") including wheat, peach, strawberry, pigeon, dog, horse, cattle, poultry, duck, rabbit, and sheep breeding. He also goes on to show in Chapter 2 many examples of variation in the wild (nature) as well, and demonstrates that the degree of variation between varieties within one species are sometimes as distinct as the variation between species within one genus. By showcasing these examples of variation under domestication and in nature he presents a very strong case against the widely held but erroneous belief in fixity of species.

In Chapter 3 he expands on the idea that many more offspring are born than can survive. This fact leads to a struggle for existence between individuals of the same species, separate species, and environmental conditions. Consequently, there are survivors and there are those that perish.

In Chapters 4 and 5 Charles Darwin thoroughly explains the concept of natural selection and argues for a strong relationship between artificial selection and natural selection. After showing in Chapter 1 the extraordinary changes of plants and animals accomplished in just tens to hundreds of years of breeding under the guiding hand of man (artificial selection) he then masterfully makes the case that these same laws of variation under the purposeless hand of natural selection could accomplish unlimited amounts of change given vast amounts of time. He captures the imagination using reasonable-sounding arguments, essentially maintaining that the power of natural selection has no limitations and can produce any complex organ given enough time. He introduces and explains his only illustration in the book, the branching tree of life, and relates this diversification of life to natural selection.

Neither does Darwin dismiss his theory's weak points. In Chapters 6 and 7 he honestly and methodically lists and grapples with various difficulties he and his colleagues have leveled against it. He concedes that there are real objections but offers various naturalistic explanations that he believes are reasonable enough to satisfy the doubts of himself and his critics.

Because his knowledge of natural history is really very good, Darwin can also discuss the evolution of complex instincts (Chapter 8) and not just the evolution of bodily forms. There are many examples of animals with different instinctive behaviors in a wide range from simple to complex. Darwin uses this fact to paint a plausible picture of how the complex instincts arose from simpler ones.

When discussing hybrids in Chapter 9 (the offspring of different species which have been bred together), he gives examples of various degrees of sterility and fertility, again showing that the boundaries are truly blurry between species. These patterns he continues to find in nature seem entirely inexplicable to him under the paradigm of Creation and fixity of each species.

In Chapter 10 Darwin discusses the imperfection of the fossil record. He is keenly aware that his theory demands countless fossil forms or "missing links" connecting the clearly defined fossil forms with each other and with those alive today. He explains their absence by maintaining that the fossil record is imperfect (incomplete) in the extreme due to erosion or periods of no sedimentation, and therefore, he says, we should not expect to find all the missing links. He also argues that the progression of organic beings (organisms) from the bottom to the top of the geologic column incompletely represents the branching evolutionary tree of life (Chapter 11).

Darwin then takes a couple of chapters (Chapters 12 & 13) to explain the geographical distribution of plants and animals in the light of his theory. Again, he understandably finds that the widely held notion of separately created, fixed species is inexplicable when he compares mainland species and island species, related flora and fauna on widely separated mountaintops, and so on. He argues that variation, natural selection, patterns and limits of colonization, vast periods of time and climate change offer a better explanation (than the views of creation popular at the time) of these geographical patterns of organic beings.

In Chapter 14 Darwin argues that similarity in morphology and embryological development strongly suggest common ancestry. Because adult animals have been shaped by natural selection to fill particular roles in the economy of nature ("ecology") it is possible for quite unrelated creatures to have *similarly* shaped anatomy, as well as for very related creatures to have very *differently* shaped anatomies. Darwin proposed that early embryological stages were better for showing kinship at the largest taxonomic levels (Kingdom, Phylum, or Class levels). He also argues why he thinks his theory is best at explaining rudimentary (vestigial) organs without any apparent use, again in response to the views of creation popular at the time.

In his conclusion (Chapter 15) he reiterates the main objections to his theory and recaps what he deems are adequate answers to those objections. He also concisely summarizes the almost unlimited power of natural selection acting on normal variability to produce the diversity and complexity of all life on earth.

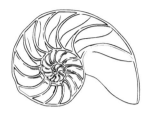

WORLDVIEW ANALYSIS

Natural Selection and Variation

Much of what Darwin said in the first four chapters was to amass a pile of evidence to convince his readers of the empirical reality that species do, in fact, vary and can change both under domestication and under nature. And indeed they do. He shows the connection between artificial selection and natural selection to persuade an uncritical mind that a little bit of change over a little bit of time can accumulate into a lot of change over a lot of time. Superficially this appears to be a reasonable conclusion. However, Darwin was unaware of something extremely important. He assumes that if species have the capacity to generate slight variations for natural selection to seize upon, these variations can then gradually add up to the improvement of the species and eventually give rise to totally new body plans and organs. He writes in Chapter 4:

> It may metaphorically be said that natural selec-
> tion is daily and hourly scrutinizing, throughout the
> world, every variation, even the slightest; rejecting
> what is bad, preserving and *adding up all that is good*;
> silently and insensibly working, whenever and wher-
> ever opportunity offers, at the *improvement of each
> organic being* in relation to its organic and inorganic
> conditions of life. (73–4, emphasis added)

In one sense, he is correct, but we need to sort the pro-
verbial baby from the bath water. A species can give rise
to a number of species, but we need to ask if there are
limits to "*adding up all that is good*" or "*improvement of each
organic being.*" Darwin is arguing that there are virtually
no limits to biological change, provided those changes are
physically possible and have survival value. The reason he
thinks we are unable to see significant change is that it
happens too slowly to detect over a human lifespan, let
alone shorter experimental time frames.

Admittedly, Carolus Linnaeus (18th century scientist
and the Father of Modern Taxonomy) believed that God
created species as fixed entities which exhibited varying
degrees of similarity and dissimilarity with other species
(hence his classification system). When Linnaeus placed
several species in the same genus, it was because they were
very similar to each other, and he assumed that similarity
was due to a very strong degree of common design, not
due to common ancestry. Later in his life he loosened his
views about fixity of species. He placed several genera in
the same family because he believed God created them to

resemble one another. Again, he saw common design, even if their similarities were not as strong as those in the same genus. Conversely, Charles Darwin superimposed an evolutionary theory on the same data. In other words, similar species could be put in the same genus because they shared a fairly recent common ancestor. Several different genera could be placed in the same family because they shared a common ancestor a bit farther back in time and so on.

Unlike many Christians of Darwin's day, our current understanding of creation biology is that God created *kinds* (not *species* in the modern, taxonomic sense of the term) with the genetic capacity to change and adapt to environmental conditions through natural selection and other factors. This means we can heartily embrace variation even to the point of speciation (when new species develop). In other words, each created *kind* had the genetic potential to diversify into a *number* of species.

Here's where we can agree with Darwin's low-level variation (what some call microevolution). When he was talking about man producing a vast array of distinct breeds we can give him a hearty "amen." When he discusses nature (via natural selection acting on variation) producing a variety of species descending from a common ancestor, all having essentially the same characteristics—again, a hearty "amen" to that. For example, it is possible that a pair of camels could have had the genetic potential to give rise to all the camels we see in the fossil record and that are alive today. And all camels are in the same family—Camelidae.

The crucial question we must ask when assessing Darwin's bigger claims is this: *Can species evolve new anatomy (body plans, organs, etc.) and new physiology simply from the accumulation of slight variations without intelligent design?* To this question, the answer is an emphatic no. No one (past, present, or future) has a valid excuse in believing Darwin's claims when they extend to this level (often called macroevolution). This holds even for people who don't know modern biology (Romans 1:20 has been and will always be true). Having some branching occur in a little "tree" (representing a created kind) isn't a problem because each twig (species) is not substantively different from all the other twigs (species) on the same tree.

We are now becoming increasingly aware of how exceedingly complex biological information is. It has become overwhelmingly clear that what Darwin called the laws of variation (this includes mutation, which is currently considered the best possible source of new genetic information) cannot make a plant or animal more complex if the genetic software isn't *already* there to make it more complex.

Biochemist Michael Behe explains the concept of *irreducible complexity* in his book *Darwin's Black Box*. His thesis has devastating implications for Darwinism. Behe explains how many biochemical systems are composed of many interacting components, where each and every component is essential for function. If just one component is dysfunctional or missing, the system won't work. (The blood clotting mechanism and the bacterial flagellum are two examples of several irreducibly complex systems Behe investigates in his book.) In short, natural selection cannot select a tenth, quarter, half, or three-quarters of the system slowly over time. It must be a *complete* system to provide a functional advantage for the organism. So in order for natural selection to work, the system has to arise all at once. This goes completely against the gradual formation of a complex organ. Darwin declares, "If it could be demonstrated that any complex organ existed, which could not possibly have been formed by numerous, successive, slight modifications, my theory would absolutely break down. But I can find no such case" (165). Maybe he couldn't find any, but Michael Behe did.

As our scientific knowledge has increased in the century and a half post-Darwin, Behe's research is not the only new challenge to the theory of evolution. Just as problematic is that over time there is a net loss of biological information through the accumulation of mutations. This is discussed in detail in the book *Genetic Entropy* by John Sanford.[5] Darwin thought lots of time was his friend. The opposite is true: mutations result in loss of information, and mutations plus time results in *more* loss of information. Millions of years doesn't fix or build things. Natural selection *selects*, it doesn't create or design. Natural

---

5. Waterloo: New York: FMS publications, 2014.

selection is like the panel of judges on *America's Got Talent*. Judges never create the talent; they only select which talent "survives" and advances to the semifinals or finals... except in natural selection's talent show, the contestants keep getting more decrepit round by round.

The laws of variation were a mystery to Darwin. Thanks to the molecular revolution over the last half century we now know quite well how biological information systems produce variation. But we also know that this variation *never* produces new, specified information. Life was created to vary... a lot! Biological information systems were designed to cut and splice, transport, shuffle, replicate, re-arrange, recombine, delete, and even mutate information. Sometimes, this can accomplish shocking and mind-boggling variation. But when we examine these variations in detail, we discover the process isn't capable of creating fresh biological information from scratch. Natural processes, without the creative hand of God, can't write new genetic programs.

Because Darwin emphasized extremely gradual change (which included additional highly complex anatomy and physiology) over vast periods of time, it was very effective in obscuring the real problem (in his own mind and in the minds of his readers). The real problem was the need for *additional genetic information*. He thought slight variations could build more complex organisms (given enough time), but he didn't understand the integrated complexity of life at every level—cell, tissue, organ, organ system, and

organism. He also didn't understand the nature of biological information, which not only manufactures the parts
but also orchestrates how the parts are put together. Only
intelligence (of an incomprehensible degree) can accomplish that. I can't overemphasize this point: variation sift-
ed by natural selection doesn't design and build new stuff.
This fact demolishes Darwin's main thesis.

The Fossil Record (Chapters 10 & 11)

There was another objection to evolution, though, that
Darwin was familiar with. The fossil record was not very
helpful in supporting his theory. Darwin writes, "Why, if
species have descended from other species by insensibly
fine gradations, do we not everywhere see innumerable
transitional forms?" (149). He fleshes the same thought
out elsewhere, "Why then is not every geological formation and every stratum full of such intermediate links?
Geology assuredly does not reveal any such finely graduated organic chain; and this, perhaps, is the most obvious and gravest objection which can be urged against my
theory" (244).

At the time, Darwin posits two explanations of why the
fossil record did not support his theory.

1. *The imperfection of the geological record.* The geological record was flawed in two major areas: the lack
   of transitional forms (missing links) between known
   groups, and the sudden appearance of many animal
   phyla during the Cambrian period. Darwin count-

ers this objection by arguing, in short, that the evidence is missing because geological processes destroyed most of the geological record. In his words, "As we possess only the last volume of the geological record, and that in a very broken condition, we have no right to expect, except in very rare cases, to fill up wide intervals in the natural system, and thus unite distinct families or orders" (290–1). So, Darwin must rely on negative evidence (an "argument from silence," of sorts). In short, he claims his theory is true, but the needed evidence was largely destroyed. However, even this is questionable. Yes, the fossil record is imperfect, but if earth history is relatively short (as I would argue), the percent of the record that is missing is a lot smaller than he envisioned. Sedimentary rock, if we match up (correlate) the corresponding strata from different regions throughout the world, seems to indicate a fairly continuous deposition of sediment. In other words, there weren't immense periods of time when there was no deposition of sediment. So, sedimentary rock worldwide captures a large fraction of geologic history, from erosion and sedimentation on day 3 of creation (when God created the dry land), to the erosion and sedimentation of Noah's flood, the erosion and sedimentation of regional flooding after Noah's flood, and beyond.

2. Darwin's second explanation for why the fossil record fails to support his theory is that *paleontology was in its*

infancy. He explains that fossils had been collected from a very small fraction of fossil-bearing rocks worldwide. He expected that with continued collecting many of the intermediate links (which were painfully absent) would be discovered in the coming years and decades. It is true that paleontology was young in Darwin's day. There have been massive amounts of collecting and studying fossil forms since 1859. Many more species have been discovered—but these have mostly served to accentuate the gaps, not to close them. If you examine the figures showing the stratigraphic ranges of vertebrate fossils in Robert Carroll's *Vertebrate Paleontology and Evolution* it is very obvious that the transitional forms between groups (families, orders, etc.) are absent.[6] Often dotted lines are drawn to connect these groups but there is no fossil evidence behind those dotted lines. But what about those fossils which *do* appear to be intermediate? *Archaeopteryx* and *Tiktaalik* are two well-known examples, but there are others. These finds are not inexplicable from a creationist perspective. Creationists believe God was extravagant in His creation of life. He created a world with an enormous continuum of habitats and a vast array of plants and animals to fill that continuum. Therefore we should expect to have living or extinct creat-

6. Robert Carroll, *Vertebrate Paleontology and Evolution* (New York: W. H. Freeman, 1988).

ed kinds that appear to be intermediate. These few interesting creatures don't prove or disprove either perspective. They can be explained by both theories.[7] Darwin was also acutely aware that fossils representing most of the major groups (phyla) of animals burst onto the scene in the lowest fossiliferous strata (Cambrian period). This phenomenon has been named "the Cambrian explosion." The sedimentary rocks below the Cambrian layer (Precambrian) are virtually barren of fossil forms. Those fossils that do exist are not considered ancestral to the phyla that appear in the Cambrian period. Again, Darwin attributes this to the imperfection of the geologic record.

> I look at the natural geological record as a history of the world imperfectly kept, and written in a changing dialect; of this history we possess the last volume alone, relating only to two or three countries. Of this volume, only here and there a short chapter has been preserved; and of each page, only here and there a few lines. (271)

The problem of the Cambrian explosion still has not been solved, but that's beyond the scope of this guide. For

---

7. For example, see my article "Pinnipeds: Blurring the Boundaries," *Answers Magazine* 8, no. 4 (2013): 68-73, last modified October 1, 2013 [accessed December 7, 2016], https://answersingenesis.org/mammals/pinnipeds-blurring-the-boundaries/.

a current and thorough discussion on this problem I highly recommend *Darwin's Doubt* by Stephen Meyer.[8]

Uniformitarianism and Bad Creationism

Interestingly, there are two major reasons why Darwin got traction with his theory: 1) Though the majority of Christians[9], both Protestants and Catholics, rejected Darwin's theory of evolution when it was first published in 1859, for several decades prior to its publication, the majority of Christians were increasingly discarding the biblical young-earth time frame and embracing vast periods of geologic time promulgated by the leading geologists of the day; 2) human reason was being increasingly exalted over the Word of God. Scripture retained authority on matters of morality but was increasingly marginalized regarding historical and scientific truth. Because the philosophies of the scientific revolution and the Enlightenment were dominant, the search for natural (secondary) laws that alone could explain natural phenomena was very much in vogue. If history and science seemed to draw conclusions contrary to the claims of Scripture, scholars generally sided with secular views of history and science.

I have already mentioned that most Christians in the half century preceding 1859 (the publication date of *Origin of the Species*) believed in very limited changes in plants and animals. The term species was not well defined, and

---

8. New York: HarperOne, 2014.

9. The word creationist was not yet coined.

even Carolus Linnaeus, the father of taxonomy, concluded towards the end of his life that biblical kinds could be broader than species, perhaps even at the level of genus.

It is likely that many Christians prior to 1859 (who believed in an old earth and rejected the idea of a global flood) believed God had created species/kinds where each currently exists.

Darwin had already rejected a young-earth view, and the varied old-earth views of Christians at the time of publication of *Origin of Species* did not satisfactorily explain many of Darwin's detailed paleontological or geographical observations. Understandably, this all contributed greatly to Darwin's disillusionment and dissatisfaction with the current views.

Not everything held by creationists of Darwin's time was incompatible with his theory. The academic community, followed by the church (for the most part), had embraced the notion of deep time (millions of years) and had jettisoned the idea of a global flood.[10] Deep time was strongly linked to the idea of Uniformitarianism, which is summarized with Charles Lyell's phrase, "the present is the key to the past." Uniformitarianism assumes that physical rates we can measure today (sedimentation, erosion, glacial movement, stalactite growth, radioactive decay rates, etc.) were operating mostly at the same rate in

---

10. Terry Mortenson, *The Great Turning Point: the Church's Catastrophic Mistake on Geology before Darwin* (Green Forest, AR: Master Books, 2004).

the unobserved past. This assumption led one to see the geologic column as the result of vast eons of sedimentary accumulation, with other geologic processes sculpting it slowly into its present form. Darwin totally embraced uniformitarianism—he devoured Lyell's *Principles of Geology* on the *H.M.S. Beagle*—and of course it gave him the time he thought he needed as he formulated his theory of evolution. Darwin reasoned that just as slow, gradual geological processes over millions of years produced the world of rock layers and fossils, so also slow gradual biological processes over millions of years produced all the diversity of living and fossil plants and animals and people from a common ancestor.

However, biblical creation holds that created kinds have an amazing capacity to vary, diversify, and adapt. The Bible also holds to a worldwide flood (Genesis 7:19). This means that terrestrial animal pairs coming off the ark were capable of giving rise to the terrestrial diversity of life on earth. It also maintains that the ark could fit them all (Genesis 7:2-3). Noah's flood also explains very well the fossil-bearing nature and transcontinental scale of the Paleozoic and Mesozoic strata.

Geographical Distribution (Chapters 12 & 13)
Christians in Darwin's time argued that species were created and placed in their current geographical ranges. Darwin saw that this didn't fit with his observations. Why was it that island species often closely resembled adjacent

mainland species? His view argued that island species were colonists from the mainland. He speculated various and reasonable methods of dispersal. Birds, bats, and their hitchhikers (seeds, parasites, etc.) could successfully colonize islands due to big storms or floods whisking them away and marooning them on islands. With many years of natural selection and adaptation to island conditions, they would become different yet similar to mainland species. Again, this is reasonable. Don't feel compelled to disagree with Darwin's ideas just because he's Darwin. Carefully consider the merits of each idea through the lens of scripture and scientific evidence.

Development, Embryology, & Rudimentary Organs (Chapter 14)

If one's starting premise is naturalism (i.e., God doesn't exist; or if He does exists, He doesn't do anything) then the only reasonable explanation to account for similarity has to be common ancestry. Remember that, because he believed that variation and natural selection can mold the adult organism to fill a particular role in the economy of nature, Darwin felt that early embryology was a better indicator for determining relationships at higher levels of classification, such as "crustacean" or "vertebrate."

For example, the adult form of a barnacle with its stationary fortress of calcareous plates bears little similarity to its fellow crustaceans. However, if we look at the barnacle's nauplius (larval) stage it shows similarity to the nauplius stage of other crustaceans. Comparing embryos (at a certain stage) of many extremely different vertebrates also reveals much more similarity than if we compare them as adults. He felt that, in a sense, organisms passed through their evolutionary history during their development. Therefore the early stages of development should represent what all vertebrates looked like in the early stages of vertebrate evolution (some fish-like ancestor).

When systematizing life, creationists can and should find relationships reflecting higher levels of classification (kingdom, phylum, class, order). In doing so, we can still say in good conscience that a fish and a bird are *"related"* in the sense that they both share the vertebrate body plan. This is *not* saying that we think that a fish and a bird have a common ancestor. We assume a relationship in that they are both created according to the basic vertebrate body plan that really exists in the mind of the Creator. In other words, the relationship is one of common *design*, not one of common *ancestry*.

God created a vast diversity of life which has varying degrees of similarity. These patterns can be interpreted as varying degrees of common design (as creationists do) or common ancestry with those species most similar sharing a recent ancestor and those most different sharing a distant ancestor (as evolutionists do). Remember that biblical creationism still holds that a number of similar species descended from a created kind (maybe family-level or genus-level depending on how big the differences are).

The current question among creation biologists is how to distinguish between relationships based on common ancestry and relationships based on common design.

Regarding rudimentary organs (today called vestigial organs) Darwin believed these were clear examples of common ancestry. When anatomical structures fall into disuse (as with blind cave fish or limbless lizards), they had no selective value and were eliminated. This is problematic from a fixity of species perspective, but not from a biblical creationist perspective. Loss of function or anatomy (or even the genetic information that codes for both) is in no way a problem to a creationist. Losing stuff can be an advantage to a species in the economy of nature (such as losing eyes in total darkness), and there are biological mechanisms for it.

It should also be noted that many structures assumed to be rudimentary (vestigial) and "useless evolutionary leftovers" are not. They have a beneficial function, though often subtle and not necessarily essential. Evolutionary assumptions may make one too quick to conclude that some structure is useless because it isn't essential, and as a result the list of vestigial organs continues to dwindle.

Once these ideas are in our bones, we can understand the thinking of evolutionists as well as our own. Evolutionists generally think that when creationists deny common ancestry, for example, we must be totally ignorant of the biological similarity in anatomy, physiology, and development found throughout living things. But they are wrong, and we needn't be threatened. They don't understand our scientific worldview, but we don't have that same luxury. We need to understand both ours and theirs. And that's why every Christian interested in defending their faith in a Darwinism-saturated world should critically read the *Origin of Species* using a fine-tuned biblical worldview.

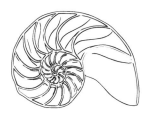

QUOTABLES

1. "There is grandeur in this view of life, with its several powers, having been originally breathed by the Creator into a few forms or into one; and that, whilst this planet has gone cycling on according to the fixed law of gravity, from so simple a beginning endless forms most beautiful and most wonderful have been, and are being, evolved."

   ~ Chapter 14 (p. 428)

2. "When we no longer look at an organic being as a savage looks at a ship, as at something wholly beyond his comprehension; when we regard every production of nature as one which has had a history; when we contemplate every complex structure and instinct as the summing up of many contrivances, each useful to the possessor, nearly in the same way as when we look at any great mechanical invention as the summing up of the labour, the experience, the reason, and even

the blunders of numerous workmen; when we thus
view each organic being, how far more interesting, I
speak from experience, will the study of natural history
become!"

~ Chapter 14 (p. 424–5)

3. "For I am well aware that scarcely a single point is
    discussed in this volume on which facts cannot be ad-
    duced, often apparently leading to conclusions directly
    opposite to those at which I have arrived. A fair result
    can be obtained only by fully stating and balancing the
    facts and arguments on both sides of each question;
    and this cannot possibly be here done."

~ Introduction (p. 2)

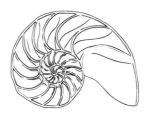

21 SIGNIFICANT QUESTIONS AND ANSWERS

1. Discuss how Darwin used variation under domestica-
    tion (artificial selection) to lay the foundation of his
    argument. Give several examples of how breeders have
    molded plants and/or animals to their own ends.

    > Darwin discusses many examples from plant
    > and animal breeding to show how much physical
    > change is possible if favored variations are select-
    > ed for further breeding. Unfavored variations are
    > eliminated. Through this process breeders can mold
    > plants and animals to their desired ends ... within
    > the genetic limitations of a created kind. Breeders
    > have done this with pigeons, cattle, horses, dogs,
    > peaches, strawberries, wheat, and countless other
    > forms.

2. Compare artificial selection to natural selection. What are some similarities and differences?

> Artificial selection and natural selection are similar in that certain variants of plants and animals are selected to live and breed, thus passing on their winning traits. Other variants are eliminated (along with their losing traits). They are different in that the selecting agent in artificial selection is the intelligent mind of a breeder that can insure a much more precise and exacting selection process. In natural selection, non-intelligent environmental conditions sift the winners from the losers. But in nature, it is often the case that the sifting of 'fit' from 'unfit' is often a sloppy, indiscriminate process. Many times it is the 'survival of the luckiest', not necessarily 'survival of the fittest.'

3. Discuss briefly why Michael Behe's thesis of irreducible complexity is a major roadblock to gradual evolutionary change advocated by Darwin.

> Michael Behe clearly shows that many processes and machines in the cell are made of many interdependent parts where each part is essential to the operation of the system. Therefore, the system is irreducibly complex. Natural selection could not select for a beneficial system unless all of its parts are there, assembled correctly, and operational in a beneficial way. Natural selection cannot select for bits and pieces to build the system gradually over vast periods of time because any incomplete system does not work and does not help the organism sur-

vive. Only the complete system helps in its struggle
for survival.

4. Briefly explain the only illustration in Origin assuming
    Darwin's premise that there aren't limits to variation
    (chapter 4).

    The branching tree of life shows that one or few
    species at the base of the tree branch into several
    species. Some go extinct and the more fit species
    survive. These in turn branch into yet more species,
    thus the tree branches more and more through
    time. Some species go extinct and the fit ones sur-
    vive and so on up the tree. As this continues, widely
    different branches will form. The species on widely
    separated branches that diverged early on, will be
    extremely different.

5. Darwin speculates how two varieties of wolves in
    the Catskill Mountains are a possible case of natural
    selection. Presuming this is true, discuss how selection
    might have worked to bring about those differences in
    the wolves.

    Darwin surmises that natural selection shaped the
    wolf variety that hunted fleet-footed deer to be tall,
    slender, and fast, while natural selection shaped the
    wolf variety that hunted sheep to be short, stocky,
    and muscular to successfully prey on stockier, stron-
    ger sheep.

6. Discuss the fundamental roadblock to unlimited change while still accepting the concept of natural selection.

> The fundamental roadblock to unlimited change is that natural selection acting on variation does not produce new genetic information. Within limits, much change can occur because of many created mechanisms to modify genetic information. It can be cut and spliced, transported, shuffled, replicated, rearranged, recombined, deleted, and even mutated, but all these mechanisms don't generate novel, specified, genetic information.

7. Discuss the types of changes possible and the types of changes that are impossible. Why is the latter impossible?

> The types of change possible are those changes that are confined to the created genetic information of an organism (microevolution). The types of change that are impossible are the evolution of completely new traits (anatomical or physiological) or body plans where the ancestor did not have those traits or body plans, nor the genetic information to code for them. The latter is impossible without divine intervention because all empirical evidence demonstrates that intelligence is required to produce new information.

8. How does variation differ from addition? Do you think
    this difference was clear in Darwin's mind? How does
    biological information relate to this difference?

    > *Variation* is different from addition because it
    > deals with the modification or rearrangement
    > of biological information that is already there.
    > *Addition* means there must be new biological
    > information added. This important difference was
    > not clear in Darwin's mind because this was before
    > any understanding of DNA and the nature of
    > information in living cells.

9. Discuss some of the ways old earth Christian views
    of creation were different when Darwin published his
    book.

    > In 1859, the predominant view of creation was dif-
    > ferent in Darwin's day in several ways. Both young
    > and old earth Christians held that the species/
    > kind could not have much variation. Only minor
    > variations could occur within a species/kind. Old
    > earthers who rejected the flood also held that the
    > species/kinds were created more or less as they are
    > today and where they are today. It wasn't biblical
    > in that it didn't consider the implications of Noah's
    > flood or the dispersal of terrestrial animals over the
    > globe after the flood. It also had adopted uniformi-
    > tarianism and a very old age of the earth.

10. Were these views of creation hard for Darwin to refute? Why?

> No, because much of old-earth thinking back then was wrong both biblically and scientifically. The old-earthers were not very attentive to the biblical text.

11. How was Uniformitarianism essential to Darwin's theory of evolution?

> Uniformitarianism required vast amounts of time to accomplish the various phenomena that it sought to explain because it relied on observable rates that are measurable in the present (which are generally very slow). Darwin's mechanism of change (assuming it could do what he thought it could) required eons of time and therefore uniformitarianism gave Darwin the time frame he needed.

12. Discuss why gradations of instinctive behaviors make evolution seem more plausible?

> Any time you show a continuum of behaviors ranging from simple to complex, it is more persuasive to argue that one could evolve stepwise into another. Nevertheless, we maintain that to go from simple to complex behaviors, it would require an infusion of some kind of biological information. Based on what we know of biological variation, there are no naturalistic mechanisms of change that would accomplish an increase in specified, complex information.

13. Discuss varying degrees of sterility and fertility in hybrids in light of created kinds?

> From a creationist perspective if organisms within a created kind can diversify into a number of species which are adapted to different environments, it is possible that changes in courtship behavior will preclude mating. Also changes in sperm and egg may exhibit a range from completely fertile to completely sterile. If fertilization occurs, there may be a range from fertile hybrids to infertile (though healthy) hybrids to unfit hybrids to natural abortion due to developmental problems. These are all easily explained within a creation paradigm.

14. What are the two major problems in the geological record that Darwin discusses?

> The first problem is the lack of transitional fossils connecting the various major groups throughout geologic history. The second problem is the absence of fossil forms connecting the dawn of unicellular life to the many disparate and complex animal body plans (represented by different phyla) present in the Cambrian rocks (the first major fossil-bearing period in geologic history).

15. Discuss Darwin's explanations that attempt to solve these problems.

> Both problems were answered by Darwin in the following way. First, if connecting fossils are never found, it is due to the imperfection of the fossil

record. This could be due to long spans of time
where organisms were never fossilized due to being
inadequately buried. Or, if they were buried and
fossilized, subsequent erosion and other geological processes destroyed many fossils showing the
evolution of life. The other explanation was that
paleontology was a young science. Darwin thought
that though the fossil record is imperfect, it would
still eventually yield fossils that would vindicate his
theory.

16. Briefly, how would a biblical creationist interpret the
fossil record using Noah's flood?

Most creationists would say that Noah's worldwide
flood of Genesis 7:19 was responsible for generat-
ing most fossil-bearing rocks that are transcontinental in scope. This would include the Mesozoic
and Paleozoic Periods. Cenozoic sedimentary rocks
are thought to be due to regional flooding, sedimentation, and fossilization after Noah's flood.

17. What patterns of geographical distribution of plants
and animals did not make sense in light of the widely
held views of creation in Darwin's day?

Darwin saw that plants and animals found on islands were most similar to the plants and animals of
the adjacent mainland. This didn't fit with the views
of creation in Darwin's day which generally held
that plants and animals were created in much their
present form and in their geographical location.

This belief wasn't biblical. It ignored the Flood and
the subsequent dispersion of land animals from
Noah's ark. It's no wonder Darwin found fault with
it.

18. Discuss how Darwin's ideas of plant and animal dispersal are very useful to biblical creationists.

Darwin's ideas and experiments on plant and
animal dispersal (particularly over oceans to
islands) provide creationists with explanations
and hypotheses for further testing on animal
transportation over the globe after disembarking
from the ark. Many Christians of the nineteenth
century believed God created everything where it
currently resides (which is not biblical at all). We
can glean from his insights while still rejecting his
time scale.

19. Discuss why rudimentary (vestigial) organs are not a
threat to informed creationists.

Darwin thought that rudimentary organs clearly
showed that evolution was at work because it was
evidence of a species losing unneeded organs over
evolutionary time. But this isn't a case of macroevolution. Losing organs is not a threat to informed
creationists because loss or reduction of an organ
is not adding novel information to the organism.
It is simply deleting, destroying, or turning off pre-
existing information. If you had a term paper that
needed to be shorter to get a better grade, deleting

several paragraphs does not require you to compose new information from scratch. Therefore, modern biblical creation can happily accept (in many cases) genetic mechanisms for losing organs, i.e. natural selection or simply by the environment turning off certain genes that results in the progressive loss of the organ. In some cases the supposed 'useless organ' is not useless at all. It may still have a function though it may not be essential for survival.

20. What did Darwin believe embryology could demonstrate?

Darwin knew that different conditions of life molded the adult forms of living things (through natural selection) in different directions. He concluded that certain stages in embryo development would more accurately reveal true relationships at higher taxonomic levels (i.e. phylum, class, or order) because the embryo is presumably less subject to the demands of nature which cause greater differences to evolve in the adult forms. For example, adult barnacles look nothing like most adult crustaceans but the nauplius larval stage reveal its true identity as a crustacean and therefore a shared common ancestor with all other crustaceans.

21. Does modern embryology strengthen or weaken
    evolution? Do the similarities in embryology threaten
    creationism?

> Although the Darwinian explanation may look
> promising superficially, as we study embryology
> and development in depth, more differences are
> revealed (even where Darwin saw much similar-
> ity). These differences are big enough that mu-
> tation and natural selection cannot solve. These
> differences that exist pose many problems with
> Darwin's view. Some of them are clearly revealed
> in Jonathan Wells's book, *Icons of Evolution*.
> Creationists expect to find similarities at many
> levels but at higher taxonomic levels they are
> assumed to be due to common design.

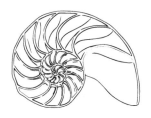

FURTHER DISCUSSION
AND REVIEW

Understand how natural selection works and be able to give examples. Be able to compare and contrast it with artificial selection.

AUTHOR
Be able to briefly summarize the major events of Darwin's life, particularly the voyage of the Beagle, and how he came to believe in evolution.

ARGUMENT
Know how Darwin built his case for evolution, with the basic proofs from natural variation that he observed in both nature and man-made domestication.

PHILOSOPHICAL ISSUES
Be able to describe what this classic is telling us about the world. Is its hypothesis supported? Be able to interact

with the following scientific questions (and any others covered in the guide):

1. What kinds of evolutionary change are possible? Give examples of possible change and impossible change. What is the difference between the two types of change and why is the latter impossible?

2. What were some problems with the views of creation of Darwin's day? How was it easy for Darwin to refute them.

3. What is irreducible complexity and why does it pose a big problem for Darwinism? Why are mutation and time Darwin's enemies; not friends?

4. What are the two major problems that Darwin discusses about the fossil record that don't support his theory? How are his theories of geographical distribution useful to biblical creationists but contrary to the creationism of his day?

5. Why does similarity (anatomy, physiology, development, & embryology) not necessarily imply common ancestry? How do we explain similarity from a creationist perspective?

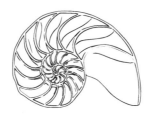

A NOTE FROM THE PUBLISHER:
TAKING THE CLASSICS QUIZ

Once you have finished the worldview guide, you can prepare for the end-of-book test. Each test will consist of a short-answer section on the book itself and the author, a short-answer section on plot and the narrative, and a long-answer essay section on worldview, conflict, and themes.

Each quiz, along with other helps, can be downloaded for free at www.canonpress.com/ClassicsQuizzes. If you have any questions about the quiz or its answers or the Worldview Guides in general, you can contact Canon Press at service@canonpress.com or 208.892.8074.

ABOUT THE AUTHOR

Dr. Gordon Wilson is a Senior Fellow of Natural History at New Saint Andrews College in Moscow, Idaho, and the author of *The Riot and the Dance*, a biology textbook. He has taught biology at Liberty University and Lynchburg College. His herpetological research on turtles was published in *Southeastern Naturalist*, *Herpetological Review*, and *The Virginia Journal of Science*, and he also makes regular contributions to *Answers in Genesis*. He and his wife Meredith have four children and a growing number of grandchildren.

48563450R00037

Made in the USA
Lexington, KY
16 August 2019